1. Bronze mirror

The back of this bronze mirror is engraved into a beautiful pattern.
The mirror was made in Britain over 2,000 years ago.

2. Celtic lady

A woman admires her reflection in the polished side of a bronze mirror.
She is wearing a bracelet and her cloak is fastened with a brooch.

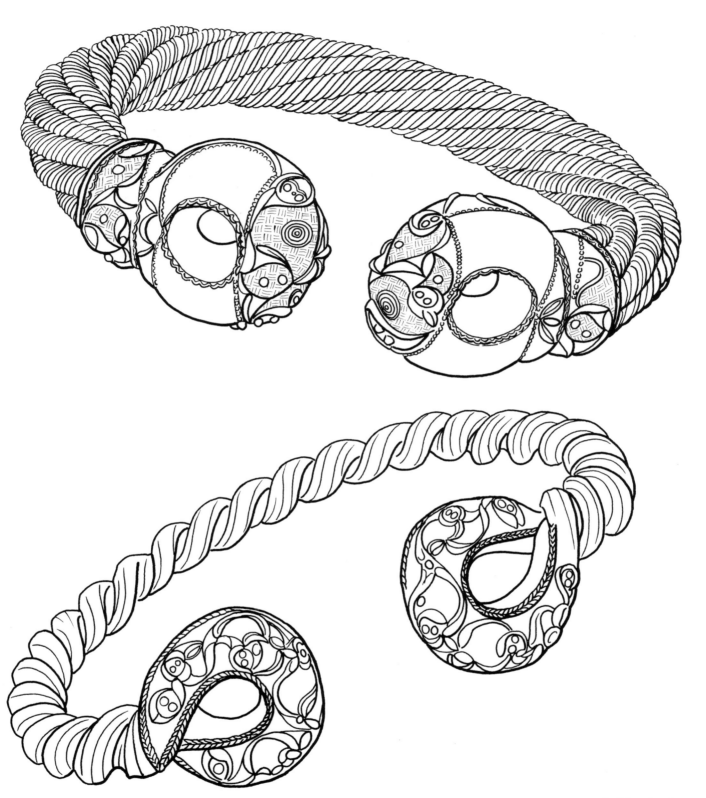

3. Neck-rings

High-status men wore neck-rings, sometimes called **torcs**,
round their necks. The torcs were made of gold and silver.
The rings were made by twisting a number of wires together.
The knobs, called **terminals**, were cast from hollow metal.

4. Headdress

A bronze 'crown' like this belonged to a warrior who lived in eastern England. He must have been a king or ruler but we do not know his name.

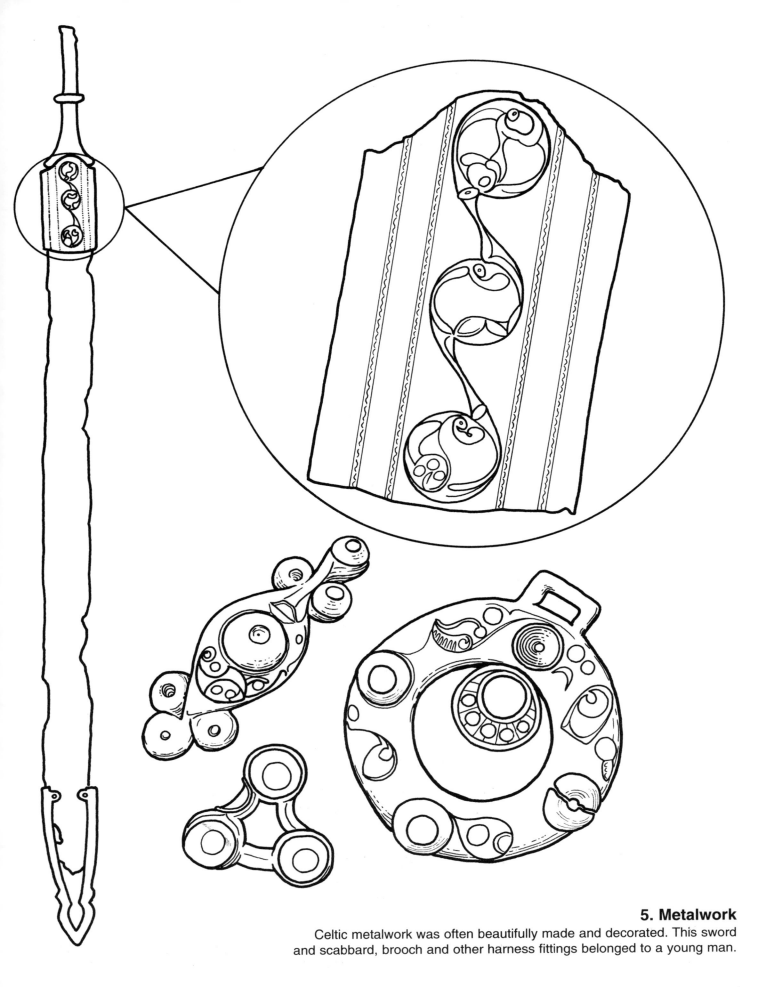

5. Metalwork

Celtic metalwork was often beautifully made and decorated. This sword and scabbard, brooch and other harness fittings belonged to a young man.

6. Shield

Celtic warriors did not wear armour but they did protect themselves with shields made of wood and leather. This splendidly decorated bronze shield was probably used for ceremonies. It is much too fine for use in a real fight.

A warrior with his chariot and horses, sword, ceremonial shield and spears is getting ready for a parade or ceremony.

8. The village

Houses in the Celtic Iron Age were round, with thick thatched roofs. Usually all the doorways faced the same way. Lots of work is going on: women are spinning and weaving woollen cloth, a woodworker is carving curvy decorations onto the wooden bowls he has made, and the smiths are tending their forge and hammering out iron spearheads.

9. At home

There is a hearth in the middle of the house for the cooking fire. The big cooking pot hangs over the fire on a chain. Behind the woman is a big stone for grinding corn, called a **quern**.

10. Ploughing

People in the Iron Age grew wheat, barley, oats and rye. This man is using an iron plough pulled by oxen.

11. Wine-jug

This fine bronze wine-jug was made in France about two and a half thousand years ago. A duck is swimming along the spout, pursued by a dog (or wolf) on the handle.

12. A face from the past

This face, with its strange headdress, and the twining animals all come from the bronze decoration on a wooden bucket.

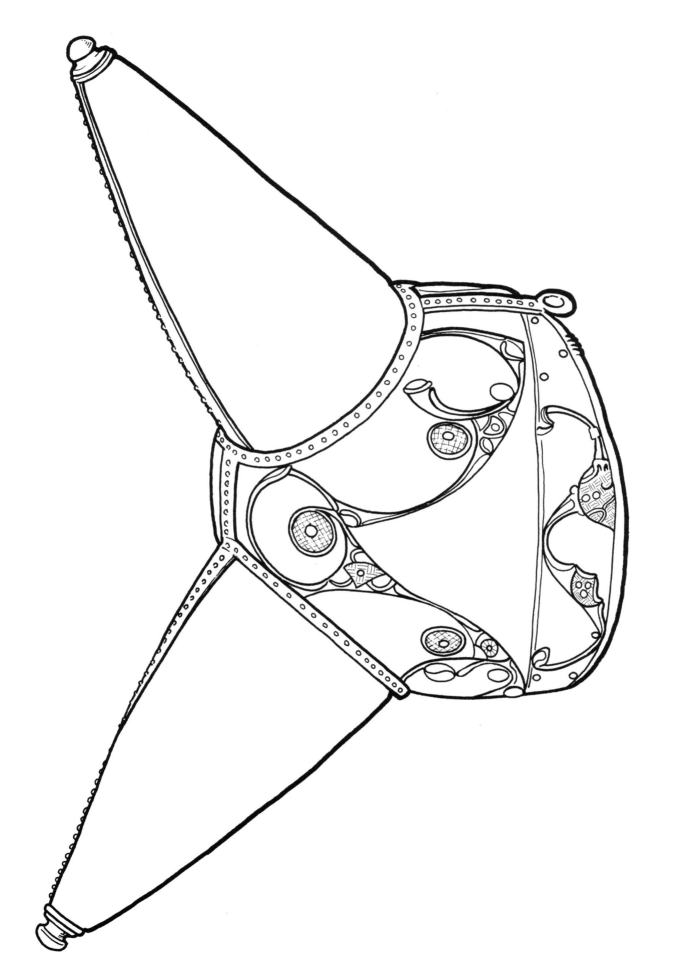

13. Bronze headdress

This bronze helmet or headdress was thrown into a river, probably as a sacrifice to the gods. Real fighting helmets did not have horns like this.

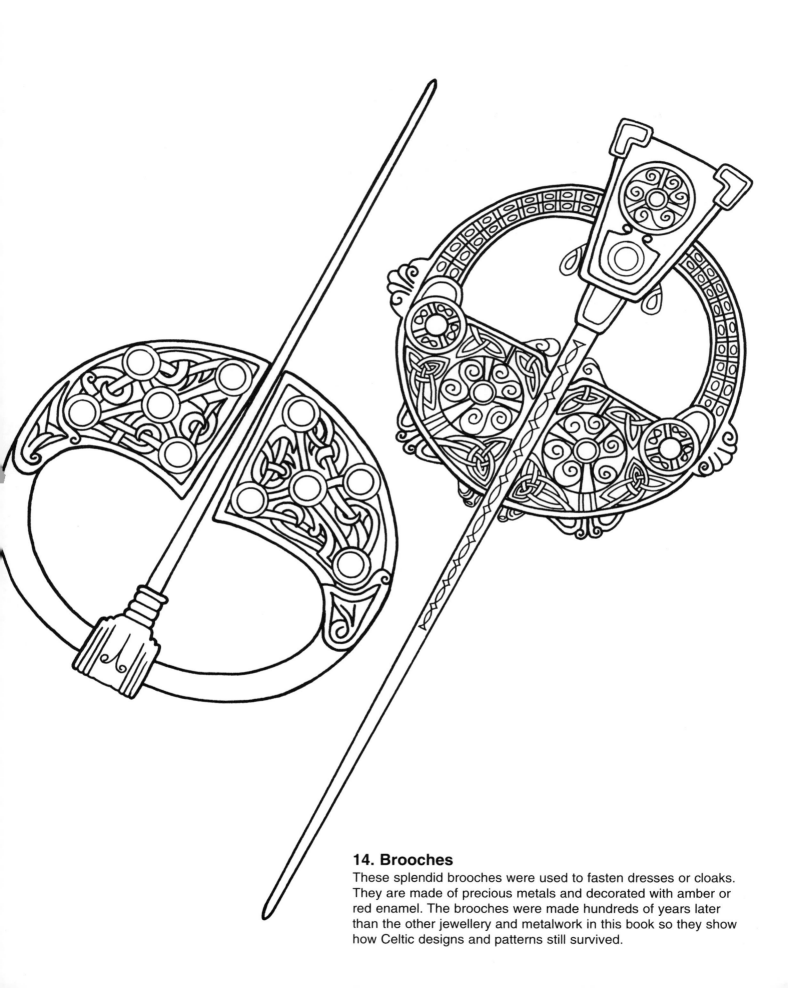

14. Brooches

These splendid brooches were used to fasten dresses or cloaks. They are made of precious metals and decorated with amber or red enamel. The brooches were made hundreds of years later than the other jewellery and metalwork in this book so they show how Celtic designs and patterns still survived.

15. Celtic coin

A coin made of gold.
One side shows a head
with elaborate hair and
a laurel wreath. The other
side shows a horse with
a man above it - perhaps
meant to be a rider, or
a charioteer.

Published by British
Museum Press
A division of the British
Museum Company
46 Bloomsbury Street,
London WC1B 3QQ

ISBN   0 7141 2133 9

Drawings by Patricia Hansom

Printed in Great Britain by
St Edmundsbury Press Ltd
Bury St Edmunds, Suffolk.